ABOUT MACROBIOTICS

Describes the wide variety of macrobiotic diet, from Japanese miso and tamari to Western wheat, oats and vegetables; with separate chapters on cereal grains, the basic food of macrobiotics; the seaweeds; Yin and Yang; and many attractive recipes.

By the same author
THE BROWN RICE COOKBOOK (with Ann Sams)

ABOUT MACROBIOTICS

The Way of Eating

by
CRAIG SAMS

THORSONS PUBLISHERS LIMITED
Wellingborough, Northamptonshire

First published 1972
Eighth Impression 1984

ISBN 0 7225 0201 X

Printed and bound in Great Britain by
Richard Clay (The Chaucer Press) Ltd.,
Bungay, Suffolk

CONTENTS

CHAPTER ONE
WHAT IS MACROBIOTICS?

'FAD DIET', 'FRINGE FOOD', 'trendy diet imported by hippies from Japan'. All these descriptions and many even more bizarre and far-fetched have been applied to an age-old way of eating, macrobiotics, that has been practised for thousands of years on every continent of the earth. Its basic precept has been so simple that it has often not even been formulated: Balance. Any history book with a description of the foods people ate, whether Incas in Peru, Chinese of the Han Dynasty, or Ancient Britons, will reveal that their diet was entirely macrobiotic, based on cereals and including other foods in season.

Eating is our most basic function. It ensures survival from day to day. It moulds our outlook on the world — the way a society eats can determine the whole structure of that society, the health and vitality of a nation's people determine the quality of life in its society. Is it really a measure of progress that a nation has thousands of doctors and hundreds of hospitals when this can only mean that its population must be plagued with sickness to be able to support such a structure? The macrobiotic person is his own doctor, a specialist in preventive medicine whose main medicine is the food he eats, the means by which he can daily ensure that he will not begin the slide into fatigue, colds, and serious illness.

Macrobiotics is revolutionary at an elemental level, for a method that brings a change in the way of eating of a people must inevitably bring a change in their way of life. In a nation where the people are free of greed, intolerance, and sickness, it must follow that exploitation, deprivation, and injustice will fall. Surely it cannot be this that excites the antagonism of some people towards macrobiotics?

Macrobiotics is a new word to describe a traditional way of

eating. It is based on the Greek roots *macros* (great) and *bios* (life), the great study of life. A macrobiotic is a person who seeks to become aware of his body's processes and through an understanding of his living environment to achieve harmony with the world around him. In music as in life, harmony brings happiness, discord and disharmony bring conflicts and unhappiness. Because the food we eat is the single most powerful factor in determining what we are, the macrobiotic uses diet as the main tool to achieve a successful balance in his life and greater joy in everyday experience. It is sometimes a difficult path, with surprises and setbacks, but full of the adventure of discovery and rewarding new insights. It is a highly personal way of eating and living, yet it embraces everything.

Macrobiotics was first brought to the West by Nyoiti Sakurazawa (Georges Ohsawa), a Japanese who in his teens was told by doctors of Western medicine that he had only a few months to live as they could produce no cure for his tuberculosis and stomach ulcers. Unwilling to accept their diagnosis, he began to study ancient Eastern medicine and, discovering the principle of yin and yang, the unification of opposites, cured himself completely. He died at the age of 74 in 1965, nearly sixty years later than the doctors had predicted, having shared his discovery with people in Japan, Europe, America, and many other parts of the world. There are now macrobiotics in nearly every corner of the globe.

There is no secret knowledge in macrobiotics. No statistical facts or scientific analyses. There is only a simple, practical method that leads to greater understanding and joy, freedom from worry, and good health. This is a book that, as you apply the ideas outlined, will have less and less usefulness. Eventually you will have no need of the information contained within and can dispense with it, or give it to a friend. Macrobiotics will have become second nature, as simple as buttoning up your coat.

If you are truly interested in harmony of mind and body, then try this method; it will cost you nothing and any discipline you may initially have to impose on yourself will be eventually rewarded by the absence of any need to curb your natural desires: true freedom. There are many words but the best way to understand it is to try it, to actually eat in this way for a few weeks. You may never look back.

CHAPTER TWO

THE TEN-DAY DIET AND THE TORTOISE

THERE ARE MANY ways to begin with macrobiotics. Some people rush in headlong with the all-grain diet or the rice diet. For ten days they eat nothing but whole grains. No oil, no vegetables, nothing but grains and a little salt. Liquids are kept to the minimum. After the first few days they may become groggy or ill as poisons accumulated from years of unbalanced eating are released into the bloodstream to be carried away. Many miraculous cures are achieved with this régime, but it can be very drastic and is sometimes overdone. Eating whole grains is providing oneself with the minimal needs to exist, and just that. Most people who begin macrobiotics have little experience in digesting cereals and the ten-day diet becomes a form of fasting, so little do they absorb from their food. After ten days the person will have become convinced of the fact that most people eat badly, too often, and too much. He will have understood an important part of macrobiotics.

It is possible to discharge accumulated poisons too quickly. There are examples of people who have eaten very badly for long periods, eating chemicalized foods, drinking alcohol, and taking drugs and medicines, who have suffered considerably under the avalanche of poisons that have suddenly been released into their blood from their safe accumulation in fatty tissue and around the organs. It may take years for a stone to form in the kidneys. As one's kidneys become stronger they will seek to discharge this foreign object. Sometimes it can be very painful if the stone is large. It is not always wise to seek too quickly extremes that your body may find difficult to deal with. It may have taken a lifetime to achieve an unhealthy state; a few years is not too long to regain health.

At the other extreme one finds the person who is like a timid bather entering the sea. At first he may simply add whole grains to his diet, gradually increasing the proportion and simultaneously reducing the amount of other items. One day he may decide to stop using sugar. He may take his favourite recipes and adapt them to include better ingredients. He will perhaps notice one day that he is feeling particularly well and will realize that this is not unconnected with his previous day's diet. Eventually he will have found a happy medium which he can then proceed to make even happier. 'Three steps forward and two steps back' is his motto. He eats well when the desire for bad foods is weak, but yields to the extremes of his appetite when they are strong. He is in no hurry, and confident of the outcome. It is usually wise not to frustrate one's appetite, for it will only rear up stronger for having been suppressed. It is only with experience that you can perfectly satisfy your body's needs and quite often a craving for a certain food reflects a genuine need. Eventually you will learn which are the best foods at any particular time, and meanwhile rigidity can only bring joylessness. It is not really so surprising to find that the person who was most strict about eating well often fails to maintain his forward drive and may spend long periods of time unwell and unhappy, eating compulsively all the foods he has denied himself for so long. One cannot alter a lifetime of acquired habits overnight, but with patience and understanding they must surely wither away.

Each person can begin macrobiotics differently, and the diets two people may eat can be as different as the shape of their faces, and yet they are both eating macrobiotically. One person may eat a diet including rice, vegetables, and Japanese foods such as miso and tamari, and achieve a healthy balance. The other may eat exclusively English foods, wheat and oats, vegetables, perhaps fish and fruit, never using rice, soya sauce, or soya paste. Yet both are eating according to the macro-biotic principles. Both are eating a diet of mainly grains and vegetables, the natural food of man.

The criteria of a macrobiotic person are not based on what he has for dinner, not upon what he takes, but upon what he gives. A macrobiotic is a person who enjoys consistent vitality and energy in every waking moment, and who sleeps deeply and restfully as soon as he gets into bed. His two basic appetites, for food and sex, are strong and healthy. He is free of anger and frustration and radiates good humour and joy to those around him. His mind is clear, his memory is sharp, and he is tolerant of all things. The person who does not answer this description, in part or in whole, is not truly macrobiotic. He may be eating the most ideal combination of foods and yet be failing to attain his goals; he must use his own judgment to find what changes are necessary. By the above criteria, there are some people who do not follow macrobiotic considerations of diet at all and yet satisfy all the aspects of good health. They are lucky people, blessed with strong constitutions, and it is to be hoped that they will always retain their qualities. Macrobiotics is a form of insurance, to maintain characteristics that are within us at birth against the influences of chaotic eating and living, and to strengthen those characteristics that have somehow been unable to develop to a point where they are the source of joyous living.

CHAPTER THREE

THE MACROBIOTIC WAY

AS YOU LEARN more about macrobiotics, you will find that you knew a lot of it already. But it is often possible to forget things, to apply them incorrectly, or to forgo them in the interests of short-run convenience. Here are a few things that are often no more than plain common sense.

Chewing

The mouth is the gateway to the digestive system. It is also one of its most important parts. In the mouth the food is prepared for entry into the miraculous process whereby it is transformed into our blood, flesh, and bones. It would be as foolish to send food into the rest of the digestive system ill-prepared as it would be to use crude oil in an automobile. We have teeth only in our mouths, so if food is not chewed well there is little hope of it being properly broken up anywhere else. Chew your food well, you will enjoy its flavour much more, you will reap immense benefits in easier digestion and you will obtain much more nutrient from each mouthful. Try to chew each mouthful fifty times.

Liquids
It is not necessary to drink more than a small amount of liquids daily. An excess of liquids leads to fatigue, strain on the kidneys and backache. Thirst is the sole criterion for using liquids. This may be difficult at first, but the rewards of a sensible liquid intake, combined with good diet, make the initial effort worthwhile.

Processed Food
Processed food should be generally avoided. Tinned and bottled foods, sugar, dyed food containing preservatives and other chemicals, foods produced with the use of chemical fertilizers and insecticides, and most commercial baked goods, are denatured versions of their original ingredients. Fresh food is living food and you can be sure it has not been prepared with dangerous chemicals. Your kitchen and digestive system are the only processing plants that should handle your food.

Local Foods
The foods that grow in your own climate are the plants which are best adapted to the seasonal temperatures in which you are also living. Therefore it is natural that they are the foods that are most likely to nourish you well. Eating fresh local foods also means that we are eating foods during the season in which they grow. So we have salads, which are light food, in the summer, and have root vegetables to give us robustness during the cold season. The cereals and pulses store well from year to year and can be eaten at all times.

Coffee and Spices
These excite the nervous system to no advantage and considerable disadvantage and should be avoided.

Animal Food
Animal food is generally inadvisable. With a balanced diet of grains and vegetables, animal products are unnecessary. Since

most animal and dairy products undergo heavy chemical
processing with hormones and preservatives, it is well if they
are not used. Fish, shellfish, wild fowl, and natural cheeses are
most advisable for those who feel a need to have some animal
food. Unless you are emotionally repelled at the thought of
animal products, remember that they are an effective way to
remedy imbalances arising from an excess of fruits and sweet
food.

Nightshades
Potatoes, tomatoes, and aubergines are members of the
nightshade family and in their underripe forms have been
known to cause epidemics of solanine poisoning where their
use has been widespread. It took the Incas of ancient Peru
several days to roast, boil, and pulverize a potato to the point
where it was considered edible. They offered them to the
Spanish invaders in the hope that they would eat many and be
unable to continue their conquest. Instead the Spanish
brought them back to Europe where they were bred into large,
tuberous food plants. Once you learn to cook well, you will
feel no nostalgic desire for these currently popular foods.

Quantity
If you chew well you will find that you are eating less. This is
good. It is wasteful and a strain to eat excessive quantities of
food, even good food. Quantity undermines quality. At a
meal, take only a little food to begin with, then take more if
you are still hungry. Try fasting completely one day each
month; it helps to give a better perspective on how often we
eat too much.

Sugar
Brown or white, honey or molasses, sugar should be avoided.
There is plenty of sugar produced from the digestion of grains
and vegetables, not to mention occasional fruit.

Salt
Natural, unrefined sea salt is an important factor in a
macrobiotic household. Too much or too little can have an
effect on the activities and appetites of a person that is
remarkable in view of the small quantity used. Each person

must find his own ideal level of salt, considering carefully the effect of his salt consumption on his level of activity and energy, his appetite for liquids and different kinds of foods, and his emotional tone. Salt has for long been a precious commodity in civilized communities and was an item of trade and exchange. The manufactured table varieties, available today are missing the wide range of trace elements that exist in an unrefined sea salt, and contain added chemicals to promote free flow. If you are in doubt as to how much salt to use in cooking, use a smaller amount and add gomasio to the finished meal if you desire more saltiness. The amount of salt you take directly influences the amount of other minerals, foods, liquids, and even oxygen that you require. It regulates your whole metabolism. It is a valuable tool for changing oneself that should be used with judgment.

Aluminium

Aluminium utensils should not be used for cooking food. If you must use aluminium, do not let food stand in the pot after cooking. Earthenware, glass, stainless steel, cast-iron, and enamel are preferred. A pressure cooker is invaluable.

Tobacco

Much is said against the use of tobacco. Most of it is true. Smoking tobacco is a habit that has no justification apart from the brief spell of peace and tranquillity it brings the addict. Yet in a sense it is a scapegoat. It bears the brunt of the blame in people's minds as the cause of cancer and a whole host of degenerative diseases. Its main deleterious effect on the user is shortness of breath, and for this alone its use cannot be justified, but a person who stops smoking and continues to eat badly, taking sugared refined foods, is not going to appreciate any great improvement in his health. As long as people are poisoning themselves in a whole variety of ways, tobacco will have a place in the spectrum, but its use must surely decline in any life-oriented society.

Drugs

There are no drugs that have a place in macrobiotics, except in the most serious emergencies. This includes stimulants, tranquillizers, antibiotics, and all drugs used for medicine or self-indulgence. A well-balanced person will have no need for drugs and will lose his freedom and health if he comes to depend upon them.

CHAPTER FOUR

THE GRAINS

THE CEREAL GRAINS are the basic food of macrobiotics. They are the combination of both a fruit and a seed and contain a perfect balance of the nutrients needed for a healthy diet. A diet of whole grains ensures a good supply of carbohydrates, proteins, vitamins and minerals in an easily digestible form. Many of our cereals exist unchanged from prehistoric times, when they nourished our ancestors. Whole cereals have been the principal food of every civilization in history and have been the objects of worship and mythology. It is only in a modern technological civilization that grains are not a principal food, indeed where there is no principal food. There are eight main types of grain and countless ways of preparing them. For the macrobiotic, a meal without grains is like a dance without music. Below are the grains described with a few suggestions for cooking them.

Whole Rice
Often known as brown rice to distinguish it from the polished talcum-dusted white version. It is the staple of the Orient, but is also grown and used in southern Europe. Land varieties exist which are being selectively bred for growing in Britain. Rice is a delicious way to balance a meal and there are many varieties — long and short-grained, sweet and savoury, glutinous and non-glutinous, brown, red, and purple. Even in countries where rice is eaten polished, the virtues of brown whole rice are known. In Thailand the army eats it daily, in China it is widely used, and insisted on for sick people, and roasted red rice is the main food of the Viet Cong.

Boiled Rice

Whole rice takes a bit longer to cook than white rice, so it is useful to cook enough for a day's use. You will soon be able to judge the amount you are using daily.

> whole rice
> 1½-2 times volume of water as rice
> salt

Put cold water, rice and salt in a pan with a tight-fitting lid, ideally a heavy cast-iron or earthenware pot, over a high flame. When the water is boiling vigorously, allow to boil for two or three minutes, then lower flame to a slow simmer. Let cook for 45 minutes to 1 hour or until all the water has evaporated. Remove lid, stir the rice, replace lid. Leave for 10 minutes, then serve.

Pressure-cooked Rice

Pressure-cooking produces less starchy grains with a pleasant chewy quality. It is an ideal way to prepare rice.

For pressure-cooking, use 1 to 1½ parts water to rice. Bring to a boil, then cook on a low flame for about ½ hour. Turn off heat and let pressure fall. Remove lid and serve.

It is possible to use tamari in place of salt in these recipes, and to add sesame seeds or a few bits of salt plum. You can also add partly cooked beans to the rice before cooking, not forgetting to increase the proportion of water.

Rice Croquettes

Add finely chopped vegetables or onions to cooked rice and add enough wholewheat flour to bind the mixture. Balls formed from this mixture can be deep-fried or fried in shallow oil in a pan.

Rice Tempura

This is another way to use left-over rice, especially if it has been pressure-cooked. Ideally cooked rice will bind together and you can take pieces of lumped-together rice and drop them into hot deep oil. They will float to the surface, and when they are slightly browned and no longer bubbling remove them and drain the oil. They should be crisp all the way through. Sprinkle with tamari.

Whole Wheat

Wheat has been the main food of the Western world for thousands of years. Excavations of prehistoric villages in Britain have yielded caches of 'emmer', a primitive variety of wheat. Wheat found in the pyramids was able to sprout after thousands of years. The Roman legions marched on stomachs full of wheat. Wheat is used for bread, the 'staff of life', as porridge, and cooked whole with vegetables. Bulgour, couscous, and spaghetti are made from durum wheat, a lighter-coloured Mediterranean variety.

Naturally Leavened Bread

Many people ask why macrobiotics don't generally use yeast as leaven in their bread. Yeasts are extremely active organisms that greatly alter the quality of the original bread dough. With fresh flour there exist already bacteria that come from the wheat grain itself, that are activated when the wheat is milled into flour, mixed with water, and put in a warm place. This is much more natural and wholesome, and the resulting bread is infinitely more flavourful.

In the evening, mix warm water with wholewheat flour to a runny batter consistency and leave in a covered bowl in a warm place overnight. The next day you will find that it has expanded and has a slightly bubbly quality. Add salt and a little oil (if desired), and add wholewheat flour until the mixture is thick enough to lift out of the bowl by hand, in one lump. Knead this dough for a few minutes or longer, then place pieces of the dough in oiled bread pans, filling them at least half full. Leave to rise in the pans for a couple of hours, then bake in an oven at 350° (Regulo 5) for 1 hour to 1½ hours. When done, remove the breads from the pans and leave to cool.

It is also possible to make breads, loaf-shaped and flat, by simply mixing wholewheat flour, salt and water into a thick dough and baking immediately. Other flours may be added to all breads, but wholewheat flour should constitute at least half the mixture.

Boiled Wheat Berries

Wheat takes quite a while to cook and a pressure cooker is very useful. Otherwise, soaking in advance speeds up the cooking time. Use 3 to 5 parts of water to wheat depending upon the dryness required. Bring to a boil and cook on a low flame for an hour, or until done. The wheat should be soft and the grains split open revealing the white interior. The wheat can be eaten as it is or fried in a frying pan that contains mixed vegetables already cooked. A traditional English food, 'frumenty', is based on wheat and currants, the currants being boiled with already cooked wheat. Cooked wheat berries can also be added to breads, made into croquettes, or used in soups and stews.

Barley

Barley is similar to wheat and makes good breads and pies, as well as creamy stews. Most barley is consumed in the form of malt beer, but this grain is delicious eaten whole.

Barley Biscuits

Mix barley flour and oil until the mixture tends to stick together and becomes malleable. Include salt and add water to make what should be a rather oily dough. Roll the dough flat on a floured board and cut discs out of the flattened dough with an upturned glass. Place the discs on an oiled baking tray and bake in an oven till brown around the edges.

Barley Stew

Mix 1 part barley with about 8 to 10 parts water and bring to the boil. Then cook slowly at a low heat, meanwhile frying carrots, onions, and finely cut cabbage in a frying pan. When the barley and the vegetables are cooked soft, mix them together and cook for another twenty minutes or so. A delicious, creamy stew.

Rye

Rye is a dark grain, similar in appearance to wheat, which makes a flour that, though sticky, produces rich black bread when used in equal proportions with wholewheat flour. Rye is much appreciated in the northern parts of Europe for its warmth-giving qualities.

Rice and Rye

Pre-soak rye grains for a few hours in water. Mix with an equal part of uncooked rice and proceed as for cooking rice, using the same proportion of water to grain. All grains can be cooked whole on their own, but combining them produces many varied and interesting dishes.

Rye-linseed Gruel
For this breakfast dish you will need a grain mill.

    1 cup rye, ground coarse   3 cups water
    2 tablespoons linseed, ground coarse   salt

Bring ingredients to boil and simmer in a covered saucepan for 30 to 45 minutes, or until most of the water is absorbed. Mix well and serve. An ideal food for anyone whose intestines are feeling tired.

Rye Crispbread

    1 cup rye flour   water
    1½ cups wholewheat flour   salt

Mix the flours and salt together and slowly add water until a very stiff dough is formed. Roll the dough as flat as possible without it breaking up and place on flat baking trays. Score with a knife to produce the shape you want the crackers to break into when baked, and bake in a 350° oven for 15 to 20 minutes or until they are crisp but not burned. They will become even crisper if allowed to air after removal from the oven.

Oats
Oats are most commonly seen at breakfast in the form of creamy oat porridge. What better way to start the day! Flaked oats are used for the refreshing summer muesli, crumbles, and oatcakes.

Baked Porridge
Long ago, in Scotland, when Bonnie Prince Charlie was on the run from pursuing soldiers, the Scots made oats by stirring the oats in water over a fire for many hours, until the desired creamy texture was attained. It was a tiresome task, stirring the porridge, and it was usually assigned to the person of least importance in the group. Acting on a tip, English troops raided

a Scottish camp and carefully examined each person there, looking for the Prince in disguise. They never looked twice at the porridge stirrer, knowing that the Prince would never be assigned such a lowly task. It was thus that Bonnie Prince Charlie went undetected and finally made his way to Skye. Now, with modern ovens, we can produce the same superb porridge with a fraction of the effort.

> 1 cup coarse oatmeal or whole oat groats
> 6 cups water
> salt

Bring the oats, water, and salt to the boil in a covered casserole on a high flame. Then place in the oven at a very low heat and leave to bake overnight. Stir and serve, with perhaps a little gomasio.

Apple Crumble

The basic crumble recipe can be used with other fruits as well as vegetables or mixtures of vegetables, beans, and grains. In a deep baking dish place sliced eating apples to about half the depth. For sweetness you may like to add a little apple juice and cinnamon or ground cloves.

The crumble: 1 cup flour   salt
    1 cup oatflakes   oil

Mix the flour, oatflakes, salt and about ½ cup oil together and work between your hands until they are well-mixed. Sprinkle over the apples and bake for about ½ hour or until the apples are soft and the crumble is crisp and brown.

Buckwheat

This dark robust grain, so popular in the winter, is botanically not a grain, but it has all the cereals' qualities. It is high in protein and warming on a cold winter day. The most yang of grains, buckwheat is usually pre-roasted to make 'kasha' before it is boiled, and is usually obtained already roasted. Quick-cooking, it provides a warm, earthy flavour that blends well with most vegetables and satisfies the heartiest appetite.

Kasha and Onions

    1 cup kasha   onions
    2 cups water   oil
    salt

Bring the salted water to the boil. Add the kasha and bring to
the boil again. Reduce the flame and it will be cooked through
in about 20 minutes. Slice the onions fine and sauté in oil until
golden. Add the cooked kasha and mix together.

Pumpkin Tempura

Cut pumpkin into pieces about ½ to 1 inch thick and 1 to 2
inches long. Make a batter with buckwheat flour, sea salt and
water that will adhere to the floured pieces of pumpkin. Dip
the pumpkin in the batter and place immediately in deep, hot
oil. When the batter is crisp and darker, the pumpkin is cooked
soft. Remove and drain the oil.

Soba

Soba is a variety of spaghetti made with buckwheat and wholewheat. It is adaptable to most spaghetti uses and can be
cooked, then fried with vegetables. Below is an ideal way to
serve it.

    1 pkt soba   chopped spring onions
    1½ pints water   toasted nori seaweed,
    tamari   broken into pieces

Cook the soba in the water, with tamari added to taste. When
the soba is cooked, place in soup bowls, including the broth.
Sprinkle with chopped onions and nori.

Millet

Millet exists in many forms around the world, the one most
common to Britain being the yellow bead-shaped variety
which cooks up light and fluffy. Millet meal adds an interesting flavour to breads and crackers.

Millet Pilaf

1 cup millet	finely cut onions, carrots,
3 cups water	cabbage
salt	

Roast the millet by stirring for 10 to 15 minutes in a lightly oiled frying pan. Bring millet, water and salt to the boil in a covered saucepan, then simmer for 25 to 30 minutes. Sauté vegetables meanwhile, adding onions first, then cabbage, then carrots, so they finish together. Add cooked millet to vegetables and mix well. Cooked beans may be added to the vegetables before adding the millet.

Millet Balls

2 cups soft cooked millet	a little chopped carrot
½ cup chopped onions	and parsley
salt	wholewheat flour

Mix the ingredients, using enough wholewheat flour to bind the mixture. Make into balls, smaller than golf balls, and deep fry in oil.

Maize

Maize is best known to many people in the form of 'corn on the cob'. But maize meal served as 'polenta' is a widespread dish in Italy and tortillas testify to maize's traditional importance in Latin America. The Hopi Indians of Arizona cultivate a blue variety remarkable for its sweetness.

On the Cob

Boil the ears in salted water for about 20 minutes. Serve hot.

Polenta

Once cooked, polenta can be mixed with leeks or other vegetables, placed in moulds, then served cold with vegetables, or cooked with dried fruit for a dessert.

1 cup polenta (or fine corn meal)
3½ cups water
salt

Bring the salted water to the boil and slowly add the polenta, stirring all the time to prevent lumps forming. Cook on a low flame for 30 minutes, stirring occasionally to prevent sticking.

Popcorn

Popcorn is a pleasant way to eat whole grains, and is a useful snack to allay hunger without spoiling appetite. It is made with oil, a saucepan with a tight-fitting lid, and popcorn kernels. Ordinary maize will not do. Heat oil to a depth of less than ¼ inch in the pan until it begins to smoke. Add popcorn to just cover the bottom of pan, and cover. As the kernels begin popping, agitate the pan over the flame. When all popping noises have stopped, pour into a bowl and add salt or tamari to taste.

Grain Mills

All grains are living food. Once they are fractured they begin to die, and lose their freshness. To a person whose main food is grains, this loss of freshness makes a difference, so whole grains are the preferred way of using them. But flours and coarsely ground grains open up a whole range of cooking possibilities, including bread, pies, porridge, soups, stews, sauces, and cereal creams.

There are several varieties of home grain mills available, with metal grinding plates, and even with small millstones. They can be attached to a table and turned by hand. They are adjustable from coarse to fine and can also be used to mill pulses, nuts, and seeds if desired. There is a great difference even between freshly milled grains and those that have been milled only a week before use, both in flavour and in quality. If a grain mill is unavailable, try to obtain the most freshly ground flours and meals available. These are usually those that are frequently used and being frequently replaced.

Whole grains should always predominate in your food. A mill is like a set of teeth, it breaks the grain into smaller pieces. Whole cereals demand more chewing, and provide work for the teeth that is necessary for their strength and health.

CHAPTER FIVE

OTHER IMPORTANT FOODS

THERE ARE SEVERAL foods used in macrobiotics that are not commonly found in most other ways of eating. Some of them are Japanese in origin, some are hard to obtain in Britain although they were used here not very long ago in some form. It is a great adventure to find European equivalents to Eastern specialities, and we learn how mustard can be used in place of ginger, or carrageen moss in place of lotus roots. The ideal is to be able to obtain every need from our own area.

Miso and Tamari

These two foods are produced by a lactic fermentation process from soybeans. They supply good quality protein as well as enzymes which aid digestion. Much of the digestive and assimilative process is dependent upon small organisms, the intestinal flora, which transmute the elements in our food into the vitamins, amino acids, etc, that the body requires. Some foods, such as meat and sugar, create gross imbalances in the flora, aggravate digestive disorders, and lead to incomplete digestion. Other foods, such as miso, tamari, naturally leavened bread, and homemade bran pickles, have a most beneficial effect on the flora situation and enhance the complete assimilation of the digested food.

Miso is often made with purely soybeans (hatcho miso) to yield a rich creamy miso with a strong flavour. A lighter miso (mugi miso) is made with miso and barley and has a milder, sweeter taste. Miso soup is excellent at breakfast and, once tried, can become a regular habit.

Miso Soup
>   2 cups finely chopped mixed onion, carrot, and cabbage
>   oil
>   salt
>   5 full teaspoons miso

Sauté the vegetables until soft, add water, and boil over 20 minutes. Add miso diluted with a little cold water and cook another 5 minutes, avoiding boiling as this harms the valuable enzymes in the miso. For a variation, add a small piece or two of wakame seaweed to the water and cook with the soup.

Miso Spread
Mix miso with tahini sesame cream, adding water to make it smooth. Chopped onion, pickle, and many other things can be added to this basic spread for bread and sandwiches.

Miso Gravy
Bring a mixture of 1 tablespoon arrowroot and 2 cups water to a boil, when it will thicken. Add diluted miso and cook a few minutes. Especially good with brussels sprouts and cabbage.

Tamari
Tamari is the purest form of soya sauce, being made by a lactic fermentation of soya beans, wheat, and salt over a minimum period of eighteen months. It can be added to most dishes whilst cooking and is used to best advantage in the kitchen. It adds a savoury flavour to soups and stews.

Tamari Broth
Boil sautéed onions in water for 15 minutes, add tamari to taste, top with chopped parsley.

Tamari Spread
Make as miso spread, substituting tamari for miso.

Umeboshi Salted Plum
These are green plums preserved in sea salt for three years. They are an invaluable aid to indigestion and all stomach problems, when they are eaten whole. A few small pieces add

sparkle to a salad and a bit before a meal stimulates the appetite.

Ume-cabbage
   cabbage
   oil
   umeboshi plums

Cut the cabbage finely and sauté in oil. When cabbage is nearly cooked, add a little water to cover the bottom of the pan and pieces of umeboshi plums with stones removed. Cover and cook 10 minutes. Serve hot, or delicious cold.

Kuzu
A medicinal form of arrowroot derived by washing whole roots in barrels of running spring water until the fibrous matter is washed away, leaving the fine powder. Kuzu is used to settle stomach upsets and to correct diarrhoea. Ordinary arrowroot is used in everyday cooking as it is much less expensive. A cold mixture of 3 teaspoons to a cup of water can be added to cooked sautéed vegetables and stirred through and cooked a further 5 minutes to give the vegetables a creamy texture. A small amount of this dilute mixture of arrowroot added to grain coffee while boiling adds body to the drink.

Lotus
The root of the Eastern water lily, a specific for respiratory problems, but very delicious as well.

Lotus Root Tempura
If using dried lotus root, soak till soft. Slice into fine rounds and drop into hot oil. Remove and drain. Should be crisp.

Lotus Hiziki
Cut lotus root into small pieces and prepare with hiziki recipe.

Mu Tea
A tea made from Ginseng root and fifteen different herbs, after a formula originally derived by Georges Ohsawa. It has a delicious flavour and a most invigorating effect. The healthy person does not need to drink it too often. Delicious hot or

cold. It is prepared by boiling a packet in 1½ pints water for about 15 minutes. The packet can be boiled at least twice, longer the second time.

Twig Tea
Also called kukicha, twig tea is made from tea leaves that have been three years on the bush, a coarse tea to look at but with a delicate bouquet. Toast the leaves until browned, then boil for a few minutes. The leaves may be boiled again.

Yannoh
A coffee made from roasted and ground grains, beans, dandelion and burdock. More than a substitute for ordinary coffee, being very rich in minerals.

Bardan
A very yang coffee made from roasted burdock roots and a small amount of chicory.

Sesame Seeds
Sesame seeds are used whole and in the form of sesame salt (gomasio) and sesame cream (tahini). Sesame oil is preferred for sautéing vegetables. Sesame salt is an indispensable condiment and quickly eliminates acidity, so is used in the event of headache. Tahini is the basis of most spreads and a small amount lends a creamy quality to stews.

Gomasio
    8 parts sesame seeds
    1 part sea salt

Roast the sesame seeds and the salt in an iron frying pan until the seeds are lightly browned and aromatic. Crush them together in a mortar and pestle until they are well mixed. It is best to make gomasio regularly as it is best used when fresh.

Houmus Tahini
A classic Mediterranean dish.

1 cup chickpeas	salt
½ cup tahini	garlic
(white unroasted)	mint, finely chopped

Cook the chickpeas in 5 parts water for several hours or until very soft. Add salt and run through a food mill or blender until creamy. Mix with pressed garlic, tahini, salt to taste, and mint. Add water to obtain a smooth consistency. A dash of tamari will enhance the flavour.

CHAPTER SIX
VEGETABLES

MOST VEGETABLES ARE used, mainly as an attractive addition to a meal based on grains. Ideally vegetables should be fresh, small, and grown without chemicals. There are many ways of preparing them, the most popular being sautéing, steaming, and tempura, for reasons of flavour and quality.

Sautéing
This method involves cooking the vegetables in a small amount of oil in a frying pan or saucepan. In order to cook thoroughly, the vegetables are first cut into small pieces. The basic method of cutting the vegetables is the 'nituke' style. To slice root vegetables nituke, first slice them diagonally into ¼ inch thick rounds, then slice these pieces lengthwise, to produce pieces the shape and size of a matchstick. Vegetables can also be grated, shredded, diced, and chopped. Vegetables can be cooked quickly by stirring them as they fry on a high flame, or more slowly, covered, with a little water added if they begin to stick. The slower method is more thorough and yields better results. If cooking different vegetables together, add them at different times so that they are all finished cooking at the same time. Generally onions are added first, carrots or radishes last.

Steaming
In steaming, the vegetables are in a porous container above boiling water, never in the water. Steamers can be obtained in

enamel or stainless steel, as well as the Japanese bamboo variety.

Tempura
In tempura the vegetables are covered in a batter made from flour and water, then deep-fried in hot oil. It is a quick method and can be applied to almost any vegetable.

Vegetables can also be boiled, made into stews, baked, pickled, and eaten in tossed or pressed salads.

Carrot Almond Nituke
3 carrots	salt
4 tablespoons almonds	water
oil	

Cut the carrots as described above, 'nituke' style. Toast the almonds in a dry pan until the insides are light brown, then chop. Sauté carrots in oil and salt. When carrots are nearly done, add water to cover the bottom of the pan, add almonds, and cover. When water has evaporated, remove from flame.

Onion Tempura
onions	salt
wholewheat flour	oil
water	

Peel onions and slice from top to bottom so the slices are held together by the core at the base. Add wholewheat flour to water to batter consistency and add salt to taste. Heat oil, dip onions in batter and place in the oil, which should be deep enough to allow the piece of onion to submerge completely. The onion will sink, then quickly float to the surface. Turn once to ensure brownness on both sides, remove and drain. If the onion piece does not float immediately, and tends to lose the batter, the oil is not hot enough.

Baked Pumpkin
Baked, boiled, in soup, or tempura, the pumpkin is a delicious autumn food. The preferred variety is called Hokkaido pumpkin, is smallish, green outside and orange inside, and is grown on a small scale in England. It is much used by diabetics

as a source of sweetness that does not upset the blood sugar balance.

Open the pumpkin, remove seeds (these can be retained and toasted for a snack), and slice into chunks. Place on a baking tray, sprinkle with a little salt, put a little water on the bottom of the tray, and bake at 350° for 45 minutes or until soft. Whole carrots or beetroots can be prepared in the same way. To avoid burned edges, cover with foil.

Pressed Salad

A little salad is always pleasant, and even in the winter months salads can be made with watercress, cabbage, or carrots. A pressed salad is made by first preparing the vegetables by cutting them very fine, even shredding them, then adding salt, and covering in a bowl under an upturned plate. Place a weight on the plate. Under pressure, the action of the salt on the vegetables will release a certain amount of juice. Save this for soups or sauces. After perhaps an hour or so depending on the vegetable, your salad is ready to serve. With a salad press of the turning screw variety, a pressed salad can be made much more quickly. A few slivers of salt plum will add a sharp vinegary flavour to a salad or a salad dressing.

Miso Pickle

Cut vegetables into small chunks and place in a jar of miso soyabean paste. After a few days remove them, slice thin, and serve as a side dish.

CHAPTER SEVEN

THE SEAWEEDS

MAN EVOLVED FROM the sea creatures. At one time all life was in and of the sea, and even now the mineral constituents of our blood correspond roughly proportionately to the mineral constituents of the sea. The sea vegetables are an excellent source of many trace elements, especially iodine, and should be eaten regularly. There are many different seaweeds and a living tradition of using seaweeds still exists mainly in Japan, China, and parts of the British Isles and Ireland. But macrobiotics on every continent are establishing a new tradition and discovering the ideal seaweeds from their own waters.

Laver (Nori)
In Wales this vegetable (called sea lettuce) is boiled, then strained for an ingredient of laver bread. In Japan it is laid out to dry on bamboo mats and the resulting sheets can be used for many purposes. It is a seaweed high in protein.

Laver Bread
    pre-cooked Welsh laver
    oatflakes

Mix the ingredients approximately half and half to form round balls that will hold together. Roll the balls out flat to make a round pancake. Fry the pancake on both sides in a frying pan, 5 to 10 minutes each side.

Rice Ball
Ideal for the lunch away from home, or for picnics and travelling, rice balls are also an excellent way to use left-over rice.
    cooked rice
    nori (Japanese dried laver sheets)
    umeboshi plum

Make a solution of water and salt. By dipping your hands in this, rice will not stick to your fingers. Form the rice into balls, enclosing a piece of umeboshi plum. Toast the sheet of nori over an open flame until its colour alters. Wrap it round the ball, and seal with a drop of water if necessary. With a plum inside, the ball will keep for days, but you can enclose vegetables, cooked aduki beans, or miso spread instead. You can also mix the rice beforehand with beans, vegetables, or chopped parsley.

Nori sheets, once toasted, can be broken up and sprinkled on soups, stews, and cooked vegetables.

Hiziki

A Japanese seaweed, hiziki resembles thick black tangled string. It makes an excellent vegetable dish and goes well with most foods.

Hiziki
hiziki   oil
water   tamari soya sauce

Rinse hiziki in cold water, then soak in water for 20 minutes. Drain and save the water. Sauté the hiziki in oil in a deep frying pan. Let cool. Add the water reserved after soaking and bring to a boil. Add tamari. Simmer uncovered for an hour or until only a little liquid remains on the bottom of the pan. For interesting variations, sautéed carrot, lotus roots, or fresh ginger can be added to the hiziki after it has been fried.

Kombu

This seaweed comes out of deep water in sheets a foot or so wide and often more than ten feet long. It has a captivating sweet/salty flavour and kombu crisps are popular with children.

Kombu Crisps

Kombu crisps are made by wiping a small square of kombu with a wet cloth, then briefly deep-frying it in hot oil. Drain and serve.

Kombu and Carrots
kombu   carrots
water   tamari soya sauce
salt   oil

With scissors, cut kombu into small squares. Soak kombu in water for 10 to 15 minutes. Boil kombu on low flame for 45 minutes, adding more water to keep kombu covered. Add a little salt and tamari, and boil 10 minutes longer. Slice carrots into rounds and sauté in oil. When carrots are half cooked, add drained kombu and continue to sauté until the carrots are completely soft.

Bladderwrack (Kelp)

Bladderwrack is commonly found on the British coast and is well known to children who pop the 'bubbles' in pieces washed ashore. It is similar to kombu and can be used in the same ways, though it is somewhat tougher. Ground into powder or granulated, it is used as a condiment.

Wakame

This delicately flavoured plant is most often used in soups, especially miso soup. It can also be lightly boiled and cooked with greens, served hot or cold.

Dulse

This reddish-purple seaweed is known as 'dillisk' in Ireland, where it is eaten raw. Its spicy flavour is not lost in cooking and it can be boiled or steamed, and then fried. It can be served on its own, or in soups and stews.

Agar-agar (Kanten)

This seaweed is used mainly for making jellies and aspics. It comes in strips or powdered, but the powdered form is more common and easier to use.

Basic Jelly

    1 teaspoon powdered agar
    ½ pint water

Bring the water to a boil and add the agar powder, stirring to ensure the powder dissolves completely. When the mixture thickens it is poured into a wet bowl or mould and allowed to set firm, in a refrigerator if quicker results are needed.

To make an apple jelly, boil chopped apples, apple juice concentrate, and a little cinnamon in the water to which the agar is added.

For an aspic, prepare grated vegetables, lightly sautéed if desired, and add to water just before adding agar. (Cooked nettle tops are particularly good served in this way.)

There are many other ways to use seaweeds, and there is one variety of nori which can be boiled to provide an excellent shampoo. Like wild vegetables, seaweeds have many properties that are small or lacking altogether in even the finest vegetables which depend upon Man's cultivation. They are an essential part of a truly natural diet and are ideally eaten in some form every day.

CHAPTER EIGHT
BEANS

THERE ARE COUNTLESS varieties of bean; most macrobiotics favour the aduki bean, the chickpea, and the black soya bean. Beans are high in protein, sweet flavoured, and blend well with most foods. They should always be thoroughly cooked until soft, and fulfil a secondary role at most meals.

Aduki Beans
The 'King of the Beans', aduki is a small red bean cultivated mainly in Japan and China. It is extremely helpful in the event of kidney problems and can be eaten in larger quantities than most beans with no attendant ill effects.

Rice and Aduki
3 cups rice	5 cups water
½ cup aduki	salt

Bring aduki beans to the boil and boil lightly for 10 minutes. Add rice and salt, bring to the boil again, then reduce heat and simmer covered for 1 hour or until all water is absorbed.

Aduki Stew
1 cup chopped cabbage	a few squares of kombu
1 cup chopped onions	1 tablespoon miso
1 cup diced carrot	salt
1 cup soft cooked aduki beans	oil
½ cup soft rice	6 cups water

Sauté the vegetables in oil, onions first, then cabbage and carrots. Add to the adukis, rice, water, salt, and kombu, and bring to the boil. Cook 30 to 45 minutes, add miso diluted in a little water, cook a few more minutes.

Black Soya Bean

The blackbean, if broken open raw, has a green interior that hints at its sweetness. Many people cook it a day before they plan to use it, as once cooked it gains sweetness with the passing of time. It is a useful food if you wish to accelerate the discharge of excesses as it has a general cleansing effect.

Blackbean and Onion

1 cup blackbeans	oil
4 cups water	salt
2 onions	

Bring the black beans to the boil in the water. Do not add salt as all beans fail to cook soft if salt is added. Simmer for 1 hour or more. If beans are pre-soaked, ideally overnight, the cooking time is reduced. Sauté the onions in oil and add salt. When the onions are golden in colour, add the black beans and stir-fry for a few minutes.

Chickpea

This bean, with its pleasant savoury flavour, is probably one of the most widely eaten beans in the world, and with good reason. It is a second staple in much of the Mediterranean.

Chickpea Fasolia

1 cup chickpeas	1 very small beetroot
4 cups water	bay leaf
2 onions	oil
2 carrots	salt

Boil chickpeas until soft. Sauté onions, then diced beetroot, then grated carrot, in oil. Add to chickpeas and add more water to cover. Simmer with bay leaf and salt for 20 minutes.

The Other Beans

The other beans are all a source for extra protein and a varied menu. Haricot, blackeye, red wonder, blue imperial pea, marrowfat pea, green lentil, soya, and mung, their names hint at the range of flavours and the different cuisines in which they are featured.

Here are a few favourite recipes.

Pease Pudding

1 cup marrowfat whole peas	oil
5 cups water	salt
1 cup chopped onion	summer savory (the
½ cup chopped carrot	natural herbal companion of all beans)

Pre-soak peas. Bring to a boil and add sautéed vegetables. Simmer for about an hour or until soft and creamy.

Slickh

A traditional Arabic dish which can be made with spinach, kale, chard, or fat hen.

1 cup blackeye beans	tablespoon chopped mint
4 cups chopped spinach	oil
½ cup bulgour (pre-soaked)	4 cups water
teaspoon lemon juice	

Cook beans for ½ hour in water. Add sautéed spinach, mint, bulgour, and simmer until beans are cooked. Add lemon juice and salt and cook dry for a further 10 minutes.

Baked Beans

5 cups haricot beans (pre-cooked)
2 cups shredded Hokkaido pumpkin
½ cup shredded beetroot
salt
oil
1 umeboshi plum, slivered
2 teaspoons celery seed
2 cloves
1 bay leaf

Sauté pumpkin and beetroot until soft, add water, and purée. Add the vegetables and herbs to the beans, adding enough water to completely cover the beans. Bake at 350° for 1 hour. The 58th variety.

CHAPTER NINE

WILD FOOD

WITH MACROBIOTICS ONE soon appreciates the truth of the adage 'You are what you eat'. One can tell from the characteristics of a food whether it is going to nourish and strengthen or not. No one would seriously consider trying to build his health on soft fruit and salad vegetables as these foods are self-evidently not suited for the mainstay of a diet. On the other hand, a vegetable that can be burned down and grows back, that displays remarkable resilience to the attacks of man and climate, that thrives even when crushed into a small amount of space with other plants, this vegetable must make good food.

Wild vegetables, or weeds, are an invaluable addition to a well-reasoned diet. One of the reasons why organically-grown vegetables are of better quality is because they come from fields where a certain amount of weed growth is permitted, even inevitable. The weeds send long roots deep into the soil and bring to the surface trace elements that disappear all too quickly on land that is used for regular vegetable crops. Needless to say, the weeds themselves are also rich in these vital trace elements.

There are several common weeds that are available from a nearby patch of common land, woods, or pasture. The main thing to watch is that the land is not agricultural land that has been treated with chemicals or is near highways where the concentration of lead 'fallout' from automobile exhausts is high.

Nettles
'The bigger the front the bigger the back.' This wild vegetable, with its painful sting, hardly attracts us at first, yet is one of the most delicious of greens available. Take gloves and a carrier

bag when collecting and prepare with gloves on. Collect only the top few leaves of the plant, they are the best, and new leaves will have grown back in a few days.

Nettle Spinach

nettles	water
oil	tamari

Chop nettle leaves fine and sauté in oil with a little salt added. When they are soft and dark green in colour, add water to ¾ inch depth in bottom of pan, tamari to taste, and cover, letting simmer until the water is evaporated. This dish has a unique savoury taste that some people compare to trout *meuniere*. For a variation add mint to the nettle leaves and omit tamari.

Nettle Soup

nettles	salt
onions	oil

Sauté onions and nettles in oil and salt until the onions are soft and translucent. Boil in a saucepan of water for at least 30 minutes. Add tamari to taste.

A few dried nettle leaves can also be boiled for tea, a traditional spring tonic, and a gargle for sore throat. The stinging element in nettles, bicarbonate of ammonia, is expelled by cooking.

Burdock

This plant is easy to recognize in the autumn as the two- and three-year-old plants produce the burrs that stick to your clothing. The root is the part eaten and is prized in the Orient for its many virtues. There it is often used as a sexual restorative and is sometimes made into a tonic soup with a whole carp. It is difficult to dig up, but well worth the effort. The young plants that have not yet formed burrs are the best as the roots have not become woody.

Burdock Tempura

burdock roots	water
buckwheat flour	oil
salt	

Scrub the burdock roots to remove the surface dirt. Parboil for
5 to 10 minutes in water to cover. Slice the roots diagonally or
'nituke' style. Mix buckwheat flour, the water from boiling the
burdock, and salt to form a batter. Dust the burdock root
slices with flour, mix with the batter, and drop tablespoonfuls
of the mixture into hot oil. Deep fry until brown, remove,
drain oil, and serve with tamari.

   Burdock can be added to vegetable dishes, but should be
parboiled or thoroughly cooked until tender.

Burdock Coffee
Burdock coffee can be made with dried cut burdock root, or
by drying fresh roots (the older woody roots can be used
here). Place the dried chips of burdock in a baking tray and
bake in an oven until they are very dark brown, but not
burned. These roasted grounds can then be boiled with water
to make a delicious coffee.

Dandelion
Both the leaves and the root of this plant may be used. In
France it is nicknamed *pissenlit* because of its great diuretic
properties. It is good food for the person who feels he has
accumulated too much liquid in his body and wishes to
eliminate it quickly. The greens are best in salad, being a little
bitter if cooked. The root is usually rather thin but can be
steamed or boiled. The root can also be made into coffee as
with burdock.

Fat Hen (Goosefoot, All Good)
Until the sixteenth century this was the most popular green
vegetable in the British Isles, known as 'melde' to the Anglo-
Saxons. Then the much larger leaved spinach was imported
and fat hen's status was reduced to that of a weed. Its taste is
very like spinach and it is ideal in soups. The seeds can also be
eaten or ground to a flour. Fat hen is rich in B vitamins,
calcium, iron, and protein. It can be sautéed with onions and
served as a vegetable, boiled with soft rice in plenty of water
for a soup, or the tops can be dipped into batter and deep
fried for a crispy tempura.

Thistle
The roots of the thistle gathered in the spring are fat and succulent and make an excellent addition to mixed vegetables. They have a slightly bitter taste, but are far from unpleasant.

Couch Grass
The roots of this ubiquitous plant can be easily found in the spring. The white shoots can be used as a vegetable, the more stringy roots can be boiled as tea. The roots can be dried and used for tea, or powdered. Couch grass is the plant to which cats and dogs are irresistibly attracted when they are ill from an excess of tinned food, and on the Continent it is added to animal feeds. In most civilized countries the diet of animals is far superior in quality to that of their human masters, and it is ironic that our society is so dependent upon animals for food which can so easily be obtained direct from the land.

CHAPTER TEN

YIN AND YANG

THE UNIQUE PRINCIPLE of Yin and Yang is the philosophical basis of macrobiotics. It is extremely simple and is understood intuitively by children and people who have achieved a good balance. It is a valuable aid to increasing one's understanding, although many people have had great happiness with macrobiotics who have never given it thorough consideration.

The theory of Yin and Yang is known as the Unifying Principle as it states that antagonistic forces are also complementary to one another. The clearest example of this is man and woman. Man and woman are opposites, yet each depends on the other for a harmonious existence. It is easy to see in man's attraction to woman the basic principle that opposites are attracted to one another, that together they are unified, each acquiring the aspects of the other. Yin and Yang helps one to understand the functioning of this interrelation in all things and through this understanding to achieve harmony.

All things may be classified as predominantly yin or yang. All things are relative, nothing is completely yin or yang, there is yin and yang in everything. Our scientists apply the concepts of acid and alkaline to our foods. Yin is the equivalent of acid, yang the equivalent of alkaline. There are several factors one can employ to determine something's yin or yang qualities.

Yang quality	*Yin quality*
Light	Darkness
Heat	Cold
Fiery, dry	Watery, damp
Hardness	Softness
Masculinity	Femininity
Active, creative	Passive, receptive
Sodium	Potassium
Animal	Vegetable
Red, orange, yellow	Purple, blue, green
Salty, bitter	Sweet, sour, hot
Grows in winter	Grows in summer
Contractive, small	Expansive, large
Heavy	Light

In selecting food, the student of yin and yang will use these factors in making a choice. If he prefers more yang food, he will choose the smaller carrots or cereal grains. The person who is eating mainly vegetable food will tend to seek the more yang vegetables.

With an understanding of yin and yang we are not surprised to find that sugar cane, a very yin substance, has a high potassium content, grows in a hot climate, has a purple colour, and a very sweet flavour. There are many seeming paradoxes in life that an understanding of yin and yang helps to resolve. The following concepts explain the dynamic relationship of yin and yang.

Yang Attracts Yin: Yin Repels Yin
Like repels, opposites attract, simple. How do we apply it? A person has a cold, a yin condition, so he eats yang food to change his condition. Yet at the same time he will take drinks

made with ginger or white radish, both hot yin foods. Yin repels yin and as he has taken the yin drink, he will begin to expel large quantities of liquid through sweating, urination, and mucus. In wars groups of men are trained to become very yang as soldiers and are then placed in opposition to other groups. Although they run towards each other it is not because they are attracted, they seek to repel one another. In the past soldiers would wear red clothing to accentuate their yang aggressive qualities. In our eating, if we eat too much salt or animal food we are drawn to take fruits and liquids, and vice versa.

Yang in Excess Produces Yin

There is the classic example of the man who is master (yang) over the slave (yin). If the master dominates too excessively he will one day find the slave no longer willing to serve him. Having become dependent on the slave's services, he will be weakened and unable to carry on. The person who depends upon foods such as meat and salt for his heat and energy will surely find that his great yangness cannot be maintained and he will become very yin. The great natural force is to balance, and any person who seeks an excess of one thing must eventually experience an excess of its opposite. The person who is showing on the surface a great deal of yang is often concealing a great deal of yin.

The Bigger the Front the Bigger the Back

This principle also states the importance of balance and moderation. In the pub on a Saturday night many people are enjoying a sense of well-being and feel extremely happy and powerful. The 'back' of this situation is revealed the morning after when the tremendous sense of good feeling is replaced by an equally tremendous sense of illness. This principle applies to all situations, from one's food to the course of entire civilizations.

A good rule to apply in using the principle of yin and yang is to employ it mainly when it can be useful because of its direct relevance to your own life. Many people become so intrigued with its exciting and often surprising ramifications that they fall victim to the principle of the 'bigger front' and acquire a great understanding of external events but have little understanding of their own selves and may not be as happy as the person who is less adventurous philosophically. Like all things, diet and philosophy have a narcissistic aspect.

The highest understanding of yin and yang is purely intuitive and is more easily obtained by the person of good health who is eating well and enjoying his food. Many macrobiotic centres are called 'Centre Ignoramus', meaning 'we know nothing'.

CHAPTER ELEVEN
LIQUIDS

IN NORMAL CIRCUMSTANCES, we lose about half a gallon of water from our bodies every day. If we are active or it is hot, more. If we are taking in more than this amount of water, then we will expel the excess in order to maintain a balanced level. This elimination process takes place by urination, sweating, and in breathing, where a lot of water is expelled in vapour form. But the process of expelling this excess places a strain on the functioning of the body, especially on the kidneys, and it is best to take only as much water as is needed.

Thirst
Fortunately a mechanism exists which enables us to be free of having to measure the exact quantity of water taken in and estimate the amount given off every day. This is the mechanism of thirst. In the absence of thirst one can be sure that the body has no need for water and that one will simply suffer the effects if an excess is taken. Some foods, such as hot foods and curries or excessively salty food, will create strong feelings of thirst that demand satisfaction. These foods should be controlled carefully.

Drinking Your Food
When food is well chewed, it becomes like water and when

swallowed is easily digested. Even a relatively dry food such as bread is nearly half water, and cooked grains and vegetables have a much higher water content. Observing your diet for one or two days will reveal that several pints of water may be consumed in food alone. In order to supply your body's need it is rarely necessary to drink more than a pint of liquid daily. Liquids are best taken either a while before or after a meal, not with the meal as they reduce the effectiveness of chewing. In the words of Gandhi: 'Drink your foods and chew your drinks.'

Water's Role in the Body

By far the greatest part of our bodies is composed of water. Water comprises ninety per cent of our blood and facilitates the transfer of vital salts and other elements from cell to cell. An excess of water upsets the normal levels of these elements in the cells. Water is the medium in which the kidneys perform their work of removing toxic elements from the blood. An excess of water does not flush the kidneys out but causes an expansion and blockage. The kidneys have to work harder and this can bring fatigue and backache. Water stimulates the wave action of the stomach and intestines by which food is passed along the digestive tract. An excess or a lack of water can inhibit this action and paralyze the intestines. Because of water's importance in the functioning of a healthy body, excessive amounts can undo the good effects of food. By following the natural requirements of thirst, and by avoiding drinking out of habit, there are no liquid problems.

Liquids should never be drunk very hot or very cold. Soups are a refreshing way to take additional liquid, as well as teas, herbal teas, grain and root coffees, and fruit juices. Fruit juices, such as apple juice or grape juice, are very concentrated drinks and should be diluted and used in small quantities. A convenient way to reduce one's liquid intake is to obtain smaller cups than usual. Usually a small amount is enough to satisfy a thirst and with a larger cup we only drink the rest 'because it's there'.

Alcoholic drinks are best avoided or taken rarely in small quantities, but their occasional use is practised by many macrobiotics. Drinks such as beer, cider, or wine made without sugar are preferred. You can usually tell if sugar has been used;

a natural beer will have a bitter, robust flavour and probably
be dark in colour, a still, extra dry cider will have a dry,
vinegary bouquet, and a good wine will not taste sweet. Spirits
and liqueurs are not recommended.

CHAPTER TWELVE

SUGAR : SWEET MISERY

IF A NUTRITIONIST or biologist from Mars were to visit
Earth, he would not be astonished that we are not green-
skinned, with hands instead of antennae. He would be amazed
instead at the fact that one of the main foods of our most
developed civilization is a poison, refined by sophisticated
technology from a crude poison, sugar cane or sugar beet.
What devitalized user of sugar would be able to explain that
sugar is 'a source of energy', that the advantages of its use
outweigh the numerous disadvantages? Constipated and irri-
table, blotchy-complexioned, probably suffering from indigestion and sinus trouble, the heavy user of sugar is a poor
advertisement for a substance which has more of the qualities
of a drug than of a food.

What Sugar Does For You

When we eat cereals and vegetables, our digestive process trans-
forms the starches of these foods into simple sugars over a
period of several hours. As these sugars are absorbed into the
bloodstream, they are stored by the body and used as required. They are essential to health and life. When sugar or
sugared food is taken, the sugar enters the blood within
minutes, raising the blood sugar level beyond a balanced proportion. The pancreas must immediately provide insulin to the
blood to reduce the level of sugar, which it does, responding
quickly to an emergency. Unfortunately, though the sugar
level may return to normal, there is usually still insulin in the
blood, which will reduce the blood sugar level to below

normal, so the body calls on its stored reserves of naturally acquired sugar to redress the balance. The pancreas has been under pressure and the body's reserves of natural sugar and the vitamins used in carbohydrate metabolism have been depleted. It is quite natural to find that diabetics, people suffering from pancreas malfunction, are often fat, reflecting heavy sugar consumption. The loss of vitamins leads to fatigue — the forerunner of sickness.

Sugar ferments in the stomach in conjunction with animal and dairy products to produce poisons which reduce the body's capacity to build teeth and bones, nerves and muscles. Its use leads to menstrual pain and acid indigestion, tooth decay and obesity. Dilute solutions of it cause internal and external inflammation and a small amount applied to a cut or sore will effectively retard the healing process. If it were discovered yesterday it would be banned and possibly turned over to the Army for weapons research.

Artificial sweeteners such as saccharine and cyclamates are, in the words of their advertisements, 'a hundred times sweeter than sugar'. They should be avoided. Manufactured glucose has all the qualities of white sugar.

What You Can Do With Sugar

There is no need to ever use sugar, white or brown. Compared to natural sweetness it has a burning taste, more hot than sweet. But it is very difficult to give up and, once abandoned, to stay away from. It is sadly interesting to read of an aboriginal tribe in the Philippines that has been discovered in the jungle, eating simple foods, living in peace and health. The anthropologists who found them did not want to 'spoil' their culture and have given them as gifts only metal axes and white sugar.

If you feel that you must have sugar, and natural sweetness from fruit and vegetables is not enough, there are milder substitutes such as honey, or barley malt extract. Below are a few recipes using no sweeteners that use the natural sweetness of fruits and vegetables to their full advantage.

Apple Fritters

apples	salt
wholewheat flour	oil
water	

Slice the apples crosswise to produce ½ inch thick circles. Mix water and flour with a little salt to a batter consistency. Add the apple slices. Heat the oil to a temperature where a drop of batter sizzles and floats to the surface. Place the batter-covered apple slices in the oil and cook both sides until browned. Drain.

Strudel

      3 apples
      1 carrot
      ½ cup raisins or currants
      ¼ cup chopped dried apricots (pre-soaked in water)
      ½ cup chopped hazels or almonds
      flour
      water
      oil
      salt

Shred or chop finely the apples and carrot and sauté in a very little oil until they become soft and juicy; add fruit and nuts and sauté on low flame for 5 minutes, with a little salt. Mix flour with oil and add water to form a pastry dough. Roll out pastry to form a rectangular sheet. Spread fruit mixture evenly over the sheet of pastry, roll the sheet carefully forward to form a long even roll. Bake in a 350° oven for 35 minutes.

Pumpkins, carrots, beetroots, and parsnips all have a sweet taste and can be used in pies, baked, or puréed. The use of a small amount of salt in cooking with sweet vegetables and fruit tends to enhance the sweet flavour.

CHAPTER THIRTEEN

SICKNESS, DISCHARGE AND MEDICINE

MOST PEOPLE, UPON becoming macrobiotic, experience real changes in their health, their outlook, and their physical form. Fat people may lose weight, while very thin people will gain weight. People who have been plagued with illness may experience physical health for prolonged periods, and people who have rarely been ill may become sick. Why?

To the macrobiotic, sickness is frequently cause for gratitude. For we know that sickness can only lead to greater health and a stronger body upon recovery. Sickness is usually a process of discharge, the expulsion of accumulated poisons and undesirable excesses that have been acquired through poor selection of food.

When we are eating well we take only that which is necessary for good health. When we eat badly or excessively we often take in quantities of salts, fats, or too much protein and carbohydrates, which our body doesn't need and with which it cannot deal. In such circumstances the excess substances are stored wherever possible and often this is in tissue round the hips, in blood vessels, around the heart, in the kidneys, or any part of the body that is not being used frequently. With good diet, the natural processes of the body begin a purification process. Our blood renews itself by about one tenth each day, so after ten days most of the accrued poisons are cleansed. The rest of the body also begins to break loose accumulations, and discharges them into the blood to be excreted. Much sickness is simply evidence of the body's efforts to discharge. So a person beginning macrobiotics may discharge mucus in the form of colds and catarrh, he may have boils, he may even, after some time, pass kidney stones. No matter how depressing at the time, we know that sickness is a sign that we are achieving sounder health.

With the improvement of the condition of one's internal organs comes an improvement of one's emotional health. In traditional medicinal diagnosis vertical lines where the eyebrows meet are a sign of liver problems. These lines give the visual impression of anger or irritation, a frown. A person suffering from the irritability that arises from a liver complaint will become more good-natured as he alleviates his physical ailment. By the same token, the anxiety arising from heart and circulatory weakness, the depression associated with respiratory problems and asthma, and the nervous problems rooted in weak intestines will be alleviated as the health of these organs is improved.

There are several ways of accelerating the course of a

sickness once it begins. The most immediate and sure thing in most cases is simply to stop eating and let the body cure itself unhampered by having to cope with additional digestion of food. A child or baby knows this instinctively and will refuse food, but adults are so used to regular meals that fasting requires a conscious effort. In fact, because sickness brings loss of appetite even in the greatest lover of food, ·a sick person may seek the worst foods because they are the only ones that can appeal to his tired palate. So we see the sick person drinking fruit juices and eating sweets because he has no stomach for real food, and thus aggravating the course of his illness.

There are a few natural medicines that can be used to accelerate discharge and alleviate unpleasant symptoms, but it is good to remember that they are still medicines. Quite often a medicine will relieve some symptoms, but can prolong the time the illness takes to run its course. Without medicine, the common cold has run its course in seven days. Is it really worth it to prolong the illness and not really develop good health afterwards just for the temporary relief of some of the more extreme symptoms? Sickness is both a warning and a punishment. It tells us that we have been doing something wrong and it causes us discomfort while the error is corrected. It should not be ignored or submerged with medicines unless very serious.

Some Simple Remedies (Internal)

Plum-Kuzu Drink
Break up an umeboshi salted plum in 1 pint of water and bring to the boil. Add a dilute mixture of a teaspoon of kuzu in a little water, when the plum water is boiling. Bring to the boil again and stir while it thickens. Tamari may be added. For colds and conditions where a discharge of excess liquid is desired, include grated fresh ginger. This drink is good for dysentery, diarrhoea, headache, colds, stomach-ache, and other intestinal discomfort.

Dentie
A special powder made with aubergine, dried, roasted and preserved in seasalt for three years. Aubergine is used because of its extreme yin quality, which is transformed into its

opposite by the extensive process of preparation. Dentie can be used as a toothpowder in the usual way and can be applied to aching teeth and sore gums for relief of pain. With a diet of grains and vegetables one need not brush one's teeth as frequently as otherwise as they do not acquire a dirty film, the gums are well exercised by chewing, and bad breath does not occur.

Chewing Stick
These sticks are used as a natural toothbrush and gum stimulant. Chew the end of the stick until the fibres have become like a brush. Then massage the gums and teeth with an upward and downward motion.

Kohren Tea (Lotus)
Steep a teaspoonful of lotus root powder in a cup of boiled water. When drunk, good for coughs and asthma.

Carrageen Moss
Boil the moss in water until the water becomes thick and glutinous. Drink for coughs and sore throat.

Aduki Juice
Boil a tablespoon of aduki in two quarts of water until half the liquid has evaporated. Add a little salt and drink for kidney ailments.

Syo-Ban
Make green tea or twig tea as usual and add a little tamari. Acts as a pick-me-up and relieves tension.

Some Simple Remedies (External)
Ginger Compress
Place cotton sack containing 4 oz grated fresh ginger in ½ gallon boiling water. Stop boiling. When water is yellowish, soak a towel in it, wring, and apply. Cover the compress with another towel to maintain the heat (it should be as hot as possible). Change every few minutes as it cools. Apply three or four times several times daily for arthritis pain, kidney pain, congestion, or piles. Apply over the abdomen for diarrhoea. Can be applied direct to most areas of pain or swelling.

Sesame Oil

A general tonic for the eyes. Apply one drop in each eye and lie down. Use a clear white oil, not the roasted variety.

Shiatsu (Finger Acupuncture)

Most macrobiotics have acquired some understanding of the principles of acupuncture. There exists a whole body of relationships between the various organs. Thus constipation can often be the root cause of a condition that manifests itself as a cold. If we understand these relationships we can more effectively deal with a problem. These are points on the surface of the skin which, if subjected to repeated pressure by the thumb or finger, will lead to a stimulation of discharge by a related organ. A vigorous massage will stimulate the whole organism and cause the organs to get rid of excess substances into the blood. Sometimes this can lead to fatigue or even passing sickness if the blood is flooded with these toxins. A study of massage and finger acupuncture is recommended, but meanwhile it is good to massage another or oneself, and to perform regular exercises, especially if one is not active at work.

CHAPTER FOURTEEN
A LIST OF FOODS

THE FOLLOWING LIST provides an indication of which foods are the most yang, and which are more yin. Yang is alkaline quality, yin is acid quality, in scientific terminology. We should always seek yang, alkaline food. Death is characterized by extreme acidity in the blood. This does not mean that we eat only the most yang foods — simply that these are generally more desirable and an alkaline balance should be maintained. Our needs vary with climate: we will desire yang food (buckwheat) in cold weather, and cucumbers (yin) more frequently in hot weather. These listings are not absolute: by

cooking a more yin food we make it more yang by applying
the elements of heat, time, salt and pressure. So a cooked
onion can become more yang than a raw carrot. If we are
eating grains and wash them down with water they create a
more acid balance. By chewing them well we are making them
more alkaline. All foods, whether listed as acid or alkaline,
should be chewed well.

These foods are listed in *categories* from yang to yin so it is
a mistake to think that an apple is more yang than a yin cereal
such as maize, for fruit in general are a more yin category. The
foods are listed in each category in order from yang to yin.

These categories overlap to some extent and should not be
followed rigidly.

Animal and Fowl
  grouse
  pheasant
  egg (fertilized)
  turkey
  duck
  pigeon
  chicken
  rabbit
  beef
  pork
  snail
  frog

In general, animal food is not necessary in our mild climate,
but is useful to the person who has let himself become weak or
anaemic and wishes to change his condition quickly. My little
daughter was offered a piece of chicken on one occasion
spat it out saying 'dirty', but her intuitive judgment does not
prevent me from satisfying the very occasional desire for a
food from this list. There is no food in macrobiotics that is
absolutely prohibited, but there are some that one quickly
learns are not useful on a regular basis.

Fish and Seafood
  caviar
  herring
  shrimp (undyed)

salmon
sole
trout
cockles
oyster
whelk
squid
carp

In general, fish is preferable to animal food. In macrobiotics we seek to eat those foods which are biologically furthest away from us. Animals are very much like people, fish less so, and grains are the most distant, being the most highly evolved vegetables, foremost in the vegetable realm as man is in the animal realm. All life, animal and vegetable, arises from a food chain that is based upon tiny plankton and micro-organisms that cannot be classified as animal or vegetable, having the qualities of both.

Cereals
buckwheat
millet
whole wheat
rice
oats
barley
durum wheat
rye
maize

In the coldest countries buckwheat is the principal grain, in Britain we eat wheat and oats. Rice is perfectly balanced and widely used in warm temperate countries, maize is most common in the warmest places.

Vegetables
burdock
dandelion root
thistle root
nettle
watercress
coltsfoot
carrot

pumpkin
parsley
onion
swede
kale
turnip
chicory

lettuce
cabbage
beetroot
lentil
peas
garlic
mushroom
artichoke

cucumber
spinach
asparagus
runner beans
potato
tomato
aubergine

The vegetables from peas onwards can be eaten sparingly or not at all. Dried pulses are much better than their underripe fresh varieties. Think of ways to use the whole vegetable: the carrot tops can be used in salad or as tempura, the beetroot tops make good greens, and the little onion roots flavour a soup. Use a brush to clean roots so as not to lose the skins.

Dairy Products
Halloumy goat cheese
goat milk
Fetta sheep cheese
Edam
Cheddar
milk
butter
cream
yogurt
clotted cream

I have a friend who one summer tried to achieve balance with yin clotted cream and yang strawberries! This is not a balanced food, but who can worry on this score in the warm (yang) climate of Devon? There are some things for everyone that override the cautions of good judgement. Enjoy them without rationalizing, occasionally.

Fruit
apple
strawberry
chestnut
cherry
blackcurrant
olive

peach
hazel
cashew
peanut
almond
pear
melon
date
fig
banana
citrus fruits
pineapple
lychee
huckleberry

It is always best to eat locally grown fruits in season. Huckleberries are rare and should be avoided altogether. Fortunately they cannot be eaten without the addition of masses of sugar, so we cannot use them anyway. Cooking brings a great improvement in the quality of a fruit, but we may find we eat less when they are raw.

Others
egoma (black sesame oil)
maize oil
sesame oil
sunflower oil
pumpkinseed oil
olive oil
groundnut oil
soya oil
margarine
molasses
honey

It is best to use a cold-pressed oil: the others are extracted by elaborate chemical processes, deodorized and decolorized. A good sunflowerseed, maize, or pumpkinseed oil still has the taste of the original seed.

Drinks
ginseng tea
mu tea

yannoh
chicory
bardan
three year tea
bancha (Japan green tea)
mugwort
peppermint
chamomile
thyme
spring water
spa water
Irish stout
beer
wine
fruit juice
sugared drinks
coffee
dyed quick-brewing tea

Three-year tea or bancha are ideal daily teas. It is best to use a small amount of drinks at the beginning or end of the list, as they are very strong. Ginseng is a powerful tonic medicine, coffee can be very destructive. We use more water than anything because we cook with it. Unless your tap water is unusual, it is better to obtain a source for natural spring water; it's well worth the extra effort.

Any list such as this is necessarily arbitrary and you should find out which are your own ideal foods by experimentation and thought. An important thing to remember is that the best of foods are degraded if they have been contaminated with toxic chemicals.

CHAPTER FIFTEEN
A SUGGESTED DIET

GEORGES OHSAWA, the founder of macrobiotics, laid out a series of diets ranging from Number 7 to Number -3. He called them the 'Ten Ways To Health and Happiness'. Diet Number 7 consists entirely of cereal grains — no vegetables, fruit, salads, animal foods, or sweets, and only a small amount of liquids. The other diets range wider and include proportionately more vegetables and other foods. At the other extreme from Number 7 the diets described allow for less than half the total quantity of food as grains, ranging as low as only ten per cent grains. When one is eating such a small amount of grains it is more difficult to maintain a healthy balance. Diet Number 7 is a most effective way to understand the importance of food to the achieving of good health but, as Ohsawa points out, the diets are *ten* ways to achieve health and happiness. It is possible to have success with any diet from the highest to the lowest, but for most of us a diet in which cereals predominate is most effective. Experience leads to the discovery of the ideal combinations and there is no strict regime, a person may take diet Number 7 one day, diet Number 2 the next. A vegetarian may include raw vegetables and fruits where another person might eat animal products, a person engaged in heavy manual labour will eat differently to a secretary. Activity is an important factor and a person's occupation will determine his needs for food. The less active person will need less food.

Below is a recommended menu for a few days, to provide variety and interest, using recipes in this book. Many people find that nothing is lost and much is gained in the way of less work for the stomach by doing without breakfast, and taking only two meals a day. When we wake up in the morning our senses are at their best, and it is possible to cloud this sharpness if too much food is taken immediately. Be flexible, if you don't breakfast, take more at lunch. No meal should be eaten unless with good appetite. Otherwise it is superfluous and is wasted.

1st Day	Breakfast	Lunch	Tea
	Baked porridge with gomasio	Rice	Pumpkin soup
		Carrot nituke Hiziki	Rice tempura
2nd Day	Miso soup	Barley stew	Nettle soup
	Unleavened bread	Kombu and Carrot	Onion tempura
3rd Day	Rice gruel	Rice	Soba
	with gomasio	Pease pudding	Parsnip chips
4th Day	Porridge	Kasha and onions	Pressed salad
		Boiled dulse	Rice croquettes
5th Day	Wheat berries	Wheat and vegetables	Rice
		Lotus hiziki	Crispy kombu
6th Day	Miso soup	Rice balls	Millet balls
	Rice tempura	Baked carrot	Sautéed cabbage
		Kombu and onions	

Needless to say, grains can be cooked in advance for use over a few days. Sometimes they will become changed in texture or appearance, especially in warm weather — they are still good to eat and easier to digest. Use them perhaps in soups and casseroles.

The ideal drinks to use are twig tea, green tea, undyed china tea, grain coffee, or herbal teas. Try putting a few drops of tamari in your twig tea.

Don't remove the outer part of vegetables, use a stiff brush to remove dirt.

Each grain of cereal is capable, in a few generations, of producing thousands of grains. As you continue to eat macrobiotically you will become grateful for every mouthful and find it hard to throw any food away.

Never sit down to a meal if you are worried, anxious, or otherwise upset. The best food will sour in your stomach if you do not take it in a relaxed frame of mind, and with appetite.

CHAPTER SIXTEEN
ON FEEDING CHILDREN

THERE ARE MANY people who have fed their children from birth on a diet of grains and vegetables. A child's life begins at the moment of conception, so much depends upon the mother's diet before and during the pregnancy. After birth, the quality of the mother's milk will depend entirely on the quality of the food she is eating. The food becomes the mother's blood, from which the milk is ultimately made.

As soon as a baby begins to develop teeth, it is time to introduce solid foods into the diet – but this does not mean that cereals cannot be fed before then. Cereals, during their maturation process, pass through what farmers call a 'milk stage'. During this period the still-ripening grains contain and sometimes exude a rich milky liquid. This liquid eventually hardens and becomes the central part of the grain. When a grain is cooked with plenty of water this part of the grain becomes creamy. With some grains such as oats, barley, and rice, this creaminess is considerable. Cereals are the only foods besides mother's milk that can provide a complete balanced diet for human requirements. With the use of a food mill it is possible to make creamy mixtures of cooked grains that will supplement the mother's milk and be very similar to it in appearance and nutritive value. Small amounts of vegetables can be added. To prepare a cereal cream, the grains should be cooked with several times the usual amount of water, then pressed through a food mill or liquidized to obtain a smooth texture.

It is also possible to prepare cereal creams for babies using finely ground flours boiled in 10 to 15 parts of water for at least 20 minutes to render them easily digestible. With a domestic hand mill you can grind your grains freshly and prepare different mixtures of grains, adding seeds or beans, and varying from fine to coarse for gruels. Kokkoh is the name used to describe a preparation of ground cereals, soya, and sesame. It can be made at home or purchased ready made. If you can prepare your own you have the great advantage of freshness.

In the absence of nursing, cereal milks of high dilution are best to begin with, getting progressively thicker as the baby grows. Occasional puréed vegetables are best included after the first few months. After several months whole rice or other grains can be prepared, but with a larger proportion of water used in cooking them than when prepared for adults.

Cow's milk is the ideal food for young calves. It promotes rapid growth (quadrupled weight in one year) and contains all the qualities needed for a calf's first steps towards maturity. It is however, a poor substitute for a food especially designed for human beings — mother's milk. If mother's milk is not available, a wet nurse should be sought — a long-standing tradition that has gone out of usage with the advent of convenient substitutes from the pastures. Otherwise, cereal creams. There are some people who use goat's milk as a food for babies, as it is the animal milk most similar in its make-up to mother's milk. If this is all that is available, it can be used occasionally.

It is important to understand your food well before shaping a child's life with it. You are forming the constitution that the child will have for all his years. It is important always to be flexible; a child will often know what is the best food at any given time and it is not wise to insist that a child eat something because you feel it is good for him. There is no cause for worry if a child sometimes refuses to eat altogether as there is surely a good reason which he understands intuitively but cannot explain logically.

A baby requires very little salt. There is often enough occurring naturally in his food without further additions. An excess of salt can produce listlessness, a desire for liquids, and crying. None at all or a deficiency can lead to inactivity. As with adults, activity is an important catalyst in the transformation of food into healthy blood. A child should be free, even encouraged, to move about on his own unrestricted by excessive clothing. Many babies are severly hampered by the weight of too many clothes. This can lead to difficulties in getting the exercise necessary for healthy growth and muscular development as well as a reduced ability to acclimatize to variations in temperature.

If a child develops a strong constitution and an appetite for good food as a result of eating well in his early years, you need not worry if his diet sometimes includes food of poor quality later on. A strong and healthy person will find it possible to take in bad foods and eliminate the undesirable elements in it without harm. Many people who grew up before World War II have extremely strong constitutions and enjoy relatively good health. It was after this period that the chemicalization of our food and environment assumed serious proportions. As a result there are many young people now whose constitutions have been weakened by a diet of denatured food from the earliest days of life. For these people the first task is to rebuild a good constitution. It is not unusual to see real changes in the shape of a person's body and his posture after a year or more of eating a balanced diet. The body has a strong natural tendency to achieve its ideal form and health. All a person must do is allow it the necessary raw materials, food and activity, to perform this work.

Those children are indeed fortunate whose parents possess an understanding of the Way of Eating and are presenting them with the most valuable birthday gift on Earth — good health and happiness.

CONCLUSION

IF YOU HAVE been eating macrobiotically for a while you will find you have learnt many things. You will have found that many aspects which were difficult at the beginning have become natural and easy through perseverance. If you have been ill, you will have found that with faith and careful thought it is possible to cure oneself without recourse to drugs and medicines.

Macrobiotics is a philosophy of freedom and happiness. This should never be forgotten. At the moment that a macrobiotic person becomes too rigid or begins to worry about his eating, he is losing the way. He could as well eat animal products and sugared foods if he is not eating every mouthful with joy and gratitude. The absence of sickness alone is not true health; a healthy person is one who lives in complete harmony with the world, to whom anger and anxiety are strangers. This is difficult, to many people it is an impossible fantasy, but to the macrobiotic it is a dream that he is always seeking to make real.

Macrobiotics is Change. It is an understanding of the power we have to change ourselves, an understanding that all life is change, that nothing exists without its opposite, that what begins must end.

With this book I have tried to say neither too little nor too much. Only through actually eating with judgement is it possible to understand the practical application of the macrobiotic way to all aspects of one's life.

RECOMMENDED FURTHER READING

Zen Macrobiotics by Georges Ohsawa
The Book of Judgment by Georges Ohsawa
Zen Macrobiotic Cooking by Michel Abehsera
Cooking For Life by Michel Abehsera
The Order of The Universe Order of The Universe Publications
The Gospel of Peace of Jesus Christ translated by Edmond Szekely
Cancer and The Philosophy of The Far East by Georges Ohsawa